D1586324

Published in Great Britain in MMXIII by
Book House, an imprint of
The Salariya Book Company Ltd
25 Marlborough Place, Brighton BN1 1UB
www.salariya.com
www.book-house.co.uk

PB ISBN-13: 978-1-908759-91-7

© The Salariya Book Company Ltd MMXIII

All rights reserved. No part of this publication may be reproduced, stored in or
introduced into a retrieval system or transmitted in any form, or by any means
(electronic, mechanical, photocopying, recording or otherwise) without the written permission of
the publisher. Any person who does any unauthorised act in relation to
this publication may be liable to criminal prosecution and civil claims for damages.

1 3 5 7 9 8 6 4 2

A CIP catalogue record for this book is available
from the British Library.
Printed and bound in China.
Printed on paper from sustainable sources.

This book is sold subject to the conditions that it shall not, by way of trade or
otherwise, be lent, resold, hired out, or otherwise circulated without the publisher's
prior consent in any form or binding or cover other than that in which it is published
and without similar condition being imposed on the subsequent purchaser.

Visit our website at **www.book-house.co.uk**
or go to **www.salariya.com**
for **free** electronic versions of:
You Wouldn't Want to be an Egyptian Mummy!
You Wouldn't Want to be a Roman Gladiator!
You Wouldn't Want to be a Polar Explorer!
You Wouldn't Want to Sail on a 19th-Century Whaling Ship!

Visit our **new** online shop at
shop.salariya.com
for great offers, gift ideas, all our new releases
and free postage and packaging.

SCOTLAND

A VERY PECULIAR HISTORY

QUIZ BOOK

With NO added
Haggis

CONTENTS

INTRODUCTION

SCOTLAND IS NOT A BIG COUNTRY. IT OCCUPIES JUST ONE-THIRD OF THE LAND MASS OF GREAT BRITAIN AND ITS TOTAL AREA IS ONLY 78,783 SQUARE KILOMETRES (30,418 SQUARE MILES). IT IS SURROUNDED ON THREE SIDES BY WATER; THE COASTLINE IS SO RAGGED THAT, STRETCHED OUT, IT WOULD MEASURE AN ASTONISHING 10,000 KM (6,200 MILES).

SCOTLAND MAY BE SMALL, BUT ITS PEOPLE HAVE BIG IDEAS, AND SCOTLAND HAS PLAYED A SURPRISINGLY POWERFUL PART IN WORLD HISTORY. SCOTTISH PEOPLE ARE FAMOUS — OR INFAMOUS — FOR THEIR RATHER PRICKLY PRIDE IN THEIR COUNTRY AND ITS ACHIEVEMENTS. IT IS NO WONDER THAT THEIR NATIONAL EMBLEM IS A PARTICULARLY VICIOUS VARIETY OF THISTLE.

WITH THIS BOOK YOU CAN HAVE FUN WITH A WIDE SELECTION OF QUESTIONS AND ANSWERS ABOUT ALL THINGS SCOTTISH. CHALLENGE YOURSELF AND YOUR FRIENDS BY TESTING YOUR KNOWLEDGE OF THE CULTURAL AND HISTORICAL ACHIEVEMENTS OF THE SCOTTISH.

PUTTING SCOTLAND ON THE MAP

QI

HOW MANY CASTLES DOES SCOTLAND HAVE?

a) 50
b) 670
c) 1,400
d) 2,000

Q2

WHICH OF THE FOLLOWING IS ONE OF THE SMALL ISLES OF THE INNER HEBRIDES, IN THE DISTRICT OF LOCHABER?

a) Isle of Whisky
b) Isle of Sherry
c) Isle of Wine
d) Isle of Rum

WHA' DEED YE CRY ME?*

THEY MIGHT ALL COME FROM SCOTLAND, BUT *SCOTS*, *SCOTCH* AND *SCOTTISH* — PEOPLE AND THINGS — ARE NOT ALL THE SAME!

SCOTS IS A LANGUAGE, SPOKEN IN THE LOWLANDS.

SCOTCH IS AN ADJECTIVE, APPLIED MOSTLY TO FOODSTUFFS, SUCH AS WHISKY, BEEF, BROTH, EGGS AND PANCAKES. TRADITIONALLY, TO CALL A PERSON 'SCOTCH' WAS OFFENSIVE — POSSIBLY BECAUSE THE WORD WAS MOSTLY USED BY THE ENGLISH (IT'S A SHORTENED, ENGLISH, VERSION OF 'SCOTTISH').

SCOTTISH IS WHAT THE PEOPLE OF SCOTLAND CALL THEMSELVES, AND ALSO THEIR NATIONAL INSTITUTIONS SUCH AS THE SCOTTISH PARLIAMENT.

BUT — JUST TO KEEP YOU ON YOUR TOES — THE CHURCH OF SCOTLAND IS ALWAYS THE CHURCH OF SCOTLAND. AND A SCOTTISH PERSON LIVING IN SCOTLAND IS ALWAYS A SCOT.

*WHAT DID YOU CALL ME?

Q3

HOW MANY PEOPLE CAN BALBRIDIE HALL IN
ABERDEENSHIRE SLEEP?

a) 5
b) 50
c) 500
d) 5,000

Q4

WHAT IS THE SCOTTISH NAME FOR PYRAMID-SHAPED
PILES OF STONES WITH HOLLOW SPACES INSIDE?

a) Cairns
b) Barrows
c) Chamber tombs
d) Pyramids

FLOWER OF SCOTLAND

ACCORDING TO LEGEND, THISTLES SAVED SCOTLAND FROM INVADERS, AND HAVE BEEN HONOURED EVER SINCE. IN AD 973, A VIKING FLEET LANDED SECRETLY, IN THE DARK, AT LUNCARTY, NEAR PERTH. PLANNING A SURPRISE NIGHT ATTACK ON THE SLEEPING SCOTTISH SOLDIERS, THE VIKINGS TOOK OFF THEIR BOOTS AND SHOES AND TIPTOED TOWARDS THE SCOTS' CAMP. HOWEVER, THEY DID NOT GET FAR. THE SEASHORE WAS THICK WITH SPINY THISTLES, AND THE STARTLED VIKINGS COULD NOT HELP CRYING OUT IN PAIN. THE SCOTTISH SENTRIES HEARD THEM, AND THE SCOTTISH ARMY WAS SAVED!

Q5

WHAT IS THE RING OF BRODGAR?

a) An ancient relic of Princess Scota.
b) A naturally occurring ring of trees.
c) A circular group of small islands.
d) 60 tall single stones standing in a circle.

Q6

WHICH OF THE FOLLOWING IS A CELTIC TRIBE NAME FROM ROMAN SCOTLAND?

a) Tugi
b) Hadrian's Wall
c) Damnonii
d) Opidii

WEE FOLK

IGNORING EVIDENCE FOUND BY ARCHAEOLOGISTS, HISTORIAN DAVID MACRITCHIE (1861 – 1925) WROTE THAT THE FIRST INHABITANTS OF SCOTLAND WERE TINY, HAIRY, EARTH-COLOURED CREATURES. HE BELIEVED THAT MEMORIES OF THEM WERE PRESERVED IN TRADITIONAL FAIRYTALES ABOUT ELVES AND BROWNIES.

Q7

HOW LONG DOES THE 750,000 CUBIC TONNES OF
ROCK THAT MAKES UP HADRIAN'S WALL STRETCH?

a) 117 km
b) 131 km
c) 146 km
d) 152 km

Q8

SOUTH OF HADRIAN'S WALL, NEAR RIDSDALE IN
NORTHUMBERLAND, A ROMAN STONE CARVING WAS
FOUND, BUT WHAT WAS IT CALLED BEFORE IT WAS
DESTROYED IN THE 18TH CENTURY?

a) Rob of Risingham
b) Roman Ramsay
c) Richard of Ridsdale
d) Nigel of Northumberland

Q9

BY AD 410 SCOTLAND WAS DIVIDED INTO FOUR
LARGE, POWERFUL KINGDOMS, BUT WHAT WERE
THEY CALLED?

a) The Picts, the Scots, the Britons and
   the Acutes.
b) The Celts, the Britons, the Scots and
   the Picts.
c) The Angles, the Romans, the Picts and
   the Scots.
d) The Picts, the Scots, the Britons and
   the Angles.

Q10

WHAT KIND OF STONE LIES AT DUNADD?

a) The sink stone
b) The footprint stone
c) The Prince's stone
d) The script stone

Q11

WHICH TRIBE LEFT CLUES TO WHERE THEY LIVED IN PLACE-NAMES BEGINNING 'PET' OR 'PIT' ('PIECE OF LAND') OR 'ABER' (RIVER MOUTH)?

a) The Scots
b) The Pets
c) The Picts
d) The Pits

Q12

WHAT WAS REPORTEDLY WASHED ASHORE IN SCOTLAND AROUND AD 900?

a) A whale
b) A 15-foot sea serpent
c) A 195-foot woman
d) A pirate ship

Q13

IN WHICH YEAR WAS THE FIRST RECORDED SIGHTING OF 'NESSIE,' THE LOCH NESS MONSTER?

a) AD 167
b) 1885
c) 1172
d) AD 565

DID YOU KNOW...?

AROUND 1100 BC, PARENTS IN NORTH-EAST SCOTLAND BUILT A TEMPLE TO DEAD CHILDREN. DOZENS OF DEAD BODIES WERE LAID TO REST IN A CAVE NEAR LOSSIEMOUTH; THEIR HEADS WERE DISPLAYED ON POLES AT THE CAVE ENTRANCE.

Q14

WHAT BUILDING DESIGN DID THE VIKING SETTLERS BRING WITH THEM?

a) Longhouses
b) Roundhouses
c) Shorthouses
d) Tallhouses

Q15

WHICH OF THE FOLLOWING VIKING WORDS MEANS 'SHELTERED HARBOUR'?

a) Dale
b) Voe
c) Ness
d) Wick

THE CELTS SPEAK

THE ROMAN HISTORIAN TACITUS RECORDED THE EARLIEST KNOWN WORDS SPOKEN BY ANYONE FROM SCOTLAND. THE SPEAKER WAS CALGACUS ('SWORDSMAN'), CHIEF OF THE CALEDONII TRIBE.

LOOKING AT THE DESTRUCTION CAUSED BY THE ROMAN INVASION, CALGACUS REMARKED, 'THEY MAKE A DESERT, AND CALL IT PEACE.'

Q16

IN 1296, IN BERWICK ON TWEED, HOW MANY PEACEFUL MEN, WOMEN AND CHILDREN WERE MASSACRED BY THE ENGLISH?

a) 5,000
b) 16,000
c) 9,000
d) 21,000

Q17

MALCOM'S MEN CAMPED AT BRAEMAR, THE COLDEST PLACE IN BRITAIN, BUT WHAT IS THE LOWEST TEMPERATURE EVER RECORDED THERE (IN 1982)?

a) Minus 17°C
b) Minus 29°C
c) Minus 31°C
d) Minus 37°C

Q18

WHAT IS THE OLDEST KNOWN SCOTTISH BUSINESS, FIRST RECORDED IN AD 1136 AND STILL GOING STRONG TODAY?

a) The Angel and Royal Hotel
b) Trinity House Lighthouse
c) Whitechapel Foundry
d) The Aberdeen Harbour Board

Q19

WHERE IS THE FEARSOME BOTTLE DUNGEON, SHAPED LIKE A FLASK, WITH NO LIGHT, NO WINDOWS, AND ONLY ONE NARROW OPENING?

a) St Andrews
b) Roxburgh Castle
c) St Pauls
d) Bannockburn

Q20

HOW LONG DID COUNTESS 'BLACK AGNES' RANDOLPH DEFEND DUNBAR CASTLE?

a) 10 minutes
b) 10 weeks
c) 10 months
d) 10 years

BAFFLING BALLS

BEFORE THE PICTS CREATED PICTURE-STONES, THEY ALSO CARVED MYSTERIOUS STONE BALLS. EACH ONE IS ABOUT THE SIZE OF A LARGE ORANGE, AND IS DECORATED WITH RAISED KNOBS OR INCISED (CUT) GROOVES AND SPIRALS. OVER 300 BALLS HAVE BEEN FOUND SO FAR IN THE LANDS WHERE THE PICTS LIVED. THEY ARE ALL BEAUTIFULLY CRAFTED, AND MUST HAVE TAKEN WEEKS TO MAKE.

WHAT WERE THEY FOR? NO-ONE KNOWS FOR CERTAIN. POSSIBLY THEY WERE ORACLES, USED TO FORETELL THE FUTURE. PERHAPS THEY WERE PASSED FROM SPEAKER TO SPEAKER AT PICTISH TRIBAL MEETINGS. OR MAYBE THEY WERE THROWN OR BOWLED FOR SPORT...

THE LOCALS

Q21

FOR OVER 40 YEARS AN ACTOR OF SCOTTISH
ANCESTRY PROVIDED THE VOICE OF WHICH CARTOON
CHARACTER?

a) Mickey Mouse
b) Popeye
c) Donald Duck
d) Bugs Bunny

Q22

WHAT FEATURE IS SAID TO CREATE A 'TYPICALLY
SCOTTISH APPEARANCE'?

a) Small ears
b) Red hair
c) Long arms
d) Big noses

DID YOU KNOW...?

SOME POETS AND BARDS CLAIM THAT KING ARTHUR LIVED IN EDINBURGH AND THAT THE MOUNTAIN CALLED 'ARTHUR'S SEAT' WAS A MEETING PLACE FOR HIS FOLLOWERS.

Q23

IN AD 208 WHO LED THE ROMAN ARMIES NORTH OF THE RUINED ANTONINE WALL HOPING TO EXTERMINATE THE ATTACKING TRIBES?

a) Emperor Antoninus Pius
b) Emperor Lucius Malfoy
c) Emperor Septimius Severus
d) Emperor Lucius Verus

Q24

WHAT LANGUAGE DO THE SCOTS SPEAK CIRCA AD 600?

a) Q-Celtic
b) P-Celtic
c) X-Celtic
d) Anglo-Saxon

I HAVE BEEN TRYING ALL MY LIFE TO LIKE SCOTCHMEN, AND AM OBLIGED TO DESIST FROM THE EXPERIMENT IN DESPAIR.

CHARLES LAMB (ENGLISH, 1775 – 1834)

Q25

WHICH TRIBE MADE AMAZING GOLD AND GARNET DECORATIONS FOR WEAPONS AND ARMOUR?

a) The Angles
b) The Britons
c) Alba
d) The Hadrians

Q26

WHICH NUMBERS DID THE CELTS BELIEVE WERE LUCKY?

a) 2 and 6
b) 3 and 7
c) 1 and 9
d) 5 and 8

Q27

WHICH OF THE FOLLOWING CELTIC MONSTERS WERE SEAL-WOMEN (AND OCCASIONALLY MEN) WHO BROKE HUMAN HEARTS?

a) Selkies
b) Glastaigs
c) Banshees
d) Kelpies

VIKING WARRIOR STYLE

RICH VIKINGS WEAR A COAT OF MAIL. IT'S MADE OF COUNTLESS RINGS OF IRON WIRE, ALL CAREFULLY LINKED TOGETHER. IT'S VERY, VERY EXPENSIVE, AND ONLY TOP WARLORDS CAN AFFORD IT. ORDINARY WARRIORS WEAR ARMOUR MADE OF REINDEER HIDE, WHICH IS PROBABLY TOUGHER!

Q28

WHICH SAINT DECIDED TO BE BRICKED UP ALIVE INSIDE HIS NEW CHURCH, AS A SACRIFICE TO GOD, AROUND AD 575?

a) St Aidan
b) St Ninian
c) St Oran
d) St Kentigern

Q29

HOW MANY BOOKS IS ST COLUMBA SAID TO HAVE WRITTEN BY HAND?

a) 10
b) 300
c) 268
d) 562

Q30

IN AD 1004, HAKI AND HEKJA WERE THE FIRST SCOTS TO REACH WHERE?

a) America
b) Australia
c) Ireland
d) France

Q31

WHO WAS CINEAD MAC AILPIN (KENNETH MACALPIN)?

a) King of the Vikings
b) Prince of the Scots
c) King of the Picts
d) Earl of Orkney

DID YOU KNOW...?

IN SHAKESPEARE'S PLAY, MACBETH MEETS THREE WITCHES: THEY ARE SCARY AND SPOOKY. HOWEVER, IN MACBETH'S TIME, IT WAS BELIEVED THAT WITCHES COULD HELP AS WELL AS HARM. THEY MADE MEDICINES AND LOVE POTIONS, CURED SICK CATTLE, RAISED WINDS, AND HAD MAGIC SERPENT STONES TO TREAT DANGEROUS INJURIES.

Q32

500 YEARS AFTER THE REAL MACBETH DIED, WILLIAM SHAKESPEARE WROTE A PLAY ABOUT HIM. OUT OF THE FOLLOWING FACTS, WHICH ONE DID SHAKESPEARE MAKE UP?

a) Macbeth gave land and money to the Church.
b) Macbeth made friends with the Vikings in Orkney.
c) Macbeth went on a pilgrimage to the holy city of Rome.
d) Macbeth had a wicked, scheming wife.

Q33

QUEEN MARGARET WAS MADE A SAINT IN 1250. WHICH OF THE FOLLOWING THINGS IS SHE SAID TO HAVE DONE?

a) Read holy books with jewelled covers.
b) Fed 20 beggars' babies every day, with a golden spoon.
c) Made Sunday a public holiday for everyone.
d) She did all of the above.

Q34

HOW DID QUEEN MARGARET DIE IN 1093?

a) She was poisoned.
b) She was killed in a battle.
c) She died of a broken heart.
d) She fell from a horse.

Q35

WHO, AROUND AD 1098, WORE A KILT, INSTEAD OF TYPICAL VIKING TROUSERS, PROVIDING ONE OF THE FIRST KNOWN REFERENCES TO KILTS IN SCOTLAND?

a) Magnus Barelegs
b) Edgar the Peaceable
c) Malcom Legbreeze
d) King William

A CLASS 'DUNCE'

JOHN DUNS SCOTUS (C.1266–1308) WAS ONE OF THE MOST BRILLIANT MEN OF HIS AGE. A FRANCISCAN FRIAR, HE STUDIED PHILOSOPHY, PSYCHOLOGY, ETHICS, LINGUISTICS AND RELIGION.

BUT HE WAS SO CLEVER THAT – AS A JOKE – HIS NAME WAS GIVEN TO VERY STUPID PEOPLE, OR 'DUNCES'.

THE STONE OF DESTINY

FROM AD 843 TO 1292, ALL KINGS IN SCOTLAND WERE CROWNED WHILE SEATED ON THIS STONE. IT WAS BROUGHT TO SCONE, IN CENTRAL SCOTLAND, BY KENNETH MACALPIN, THE FIRST KING TO RULE BOTH DAL RIATA AND PICTLAND.

AFTER CAPTURING IT IN 1296, EDWARD I'S TROOPS ANNOUNCED THAT THEY WERE TAKING IT AWAY TO LONDON, WHERE IT BECAME PART OF THE CORONATION THRONE USED BY ALL ENGLISH KINGS AND QUEENS. BUT SCOTTISH LEGENDS TELL HOW THE REAL STONE WAS HIDDEN BY THE MONKS OF SCONE ABBEY, WHO GAVE THE ENGLISH A FAKE STONE INSTEAD — SOME SAY, AN OLD STONE DRAIN-COVER FROM THE MONKS' LAVATORY! THE SCOTTISH LEGENDS SAY THAT THEY HID THE ORIGINAL ON DUNSINNAN HILL — OR POSSIBLY UNDER ROSSLYN CHAPEL, NEAR EDINBURGH.

THE STONE OF DESTINY (REAL OR FAKE) WAS 'KIDNAPPED' FROM WESTMINSTER ABBEY IN LONDON BY SCOTTISH STUDENTS IN 1950. IT WAS FOUND IN ARBROATH ABBEY, RETURNED TO LONDON, AND THEN OFFICIALLY GIVEN BACK TO SCOTLAND IN 1996. TODAY, IT IS ON DISPLAY IN EDINBURGH CASTLE. SCIENTIFIC TESTS HAVE SUGGESTED THAT IT MAY BE THE REAL STONE OF DESTINY AFTER ALL.

Q36

HOW DID SIX-YEAR-OLD MARGARET, THE MAID OF NORWAY, DIE IN AD 1290?

a) In a shipwreck
b) Severe seasickness
c) It is unknown.
d) She fell from a tree.

Q37

WHO DID ROBERT THE BRUCE STAB TO DEATH IN A CHURCH IN DUMFRIES?

a) William Wallace
b) The Countess of Carrick
c) Red John Comyn
d) Mel Gibson

DID YOU KNOW?

ROBERT THE BRUCE POSSIBLY INHERITED HIS RUTHLESS STREAK FROM HIS MOTHER, THE COUNTESS OF CARRICK. BEFORE BRUCE WAS BORN, SHE IS SAID TO HAVE SEEN A HANDSOME KNIGHT, MUCH YOUNGER THAN SHE WAS, RIDING PAST HER CASTLE — AND KIDNAPPED HIM. HE BECAME BRUCE'S FATHER.

Q38

HOW DID KING ROBERT THE BRUCE DIE IN AD 1329?

a) In battle
b) Leprosy
c) His head was split in two by a battle-axe.
d) Of old age

Q39

WHAT DID GRIEVING WIDOW DEVORGUILLA BALLIOL DO WITH HER DEAD HUSBAND'S HEART?

a) She ate it.
b) She sold it.
c) She had it framed and mounted on the wall.
d) She wore it like a jewel.

Q40

HOW MUCH OF SCOTLAND'S POPULATION PERISHED AFTER THE ARRIVAL OF THE PLAGUE?

a) All of it
b) One half
c) One third
d) Three quarters

WORK AND PLAY

Q41

WHICH ENCYCLOPAEDIA WAS FIRST COMPILED BETWEEN 1768–1781 IN EDINBURGH AND IS STILL IN PRINT TODAY?

a) *Wikipedia*
b) *Lexicon Technicum*
c) *Encyclopaedia Britannica*
d) *Encyclopaedia Perthensis*

Q42

WHICH OF THE FOLLOWING WAS *NOT* INVENTED IN SCOTLAND OR BY A SCOTSMAN?

a) Scotch egg
b) Sherlock Holmes
c) Waterproof coats
d) Bicycles

Q43

WHAT IS GNEISS?

a) A Scottish pastry
b) A breed of sheep
c) A type of rock
d) A broth

" THERE IS A GREAT PECULIARITY ABOUT THE HIGHLANDS AND HIGHLANDERS… "

QUEEN VICTORIA
(ENGLISH/GERMAN, 1819–1901)

DID YOU KNOW...?

THE STUDY OF ROCKS AND THE EARTH'S ROTATION WAS PIONEERED BY JAMES HUTTON (1726–1797). 'YOUR COUNTRY [SCOTLAND] CONSISTS OF TWO THINGS, STONE AND WATER.'
(DR SAMUEL JOHNSON, 1709–1784)

Q44

ACCORDING TO A SCOTTISH PROVERB, WHAT MAKES A REBELLION ALONG WITH TWELVE HIGHLANDERS?

a) A herd of Highland cows
b) A bagpipe
c) A fiddle and a flute
d) Twelve of the Highlanders' wives

Q45

DURING THE BRONZE AGE, WHAT DID PEOPLE EAT
EITHER RAW (CHEWY AND CRUNCHY) OR TOASTED
ON A FLAT STONE BY THE FIRE TO MAKE IT CRISP?

a) Sillocks (baby fish)
b) Young deer's horn
c) Seaweed
d) Grass

ROMAN FORTS AND ROMAN NAILS

THE FORT AT INCHTUTHIL WAS ABANDONED BY THE ROMANS IN
AD 86–87, AS IT WAS TOO DIFFICULT TO GUARD AND KEEP
SUPPLIED AMIDST HOSTILE TERRITORY. SINCE THEN, OVER A
MILLION ROMAN IRON NAILS HAVE BEEN FOUND AT THE SITE.
MANY HAVE BEEN SOLD TO CHRISTIAN GROUPS ALL AROUND
THE WORLD – BECAUSE THEY ARE FROM AROUND THE SAME
DATE AS THE NAILS WITH WHICH JESUS CHRIST WAS CRUCIFIED.

Q46

BRONZE WAS KNOWN AS 'THE WORK OF THE GODS' AND IS A METAL ALLOY, BUT WHAT TWO METALS IS IT MADE FROM?

a) Copper and zinc
b) Iron and carbon
c) Tin and lead
d) Copper and tin

THE PERFECT VIKING YEAR

WINTER: AT HOME, FEASTING WITH WARRIORS
EARLY SPRING: SOWING CROPS ON THE FARM
LATE SPRING: GOING ON VIKING RAIDS TO IRELAND AND THE HEBRIDES
SUMMER: AT HOME, HARVESTING
AUTUMN: RAIDING AGAIN!

To keep warm, everyone in Scotland wore the same kinds of clothes: cloaks, tunics and long trousers, just like the Pictish warrior portrayed on the famous Rhynie stone, carved around AD 700. Tunics were short for men and below the knee for women; trousers were for men only. Men and women grew their hair long, and may have dyed or bleached it.

Q47

In 1159 BC what covered the sky and blocked out the sun for 20 years?

a) Ash and gas from the Hekla Volcano in Iceland
b) It is unknown
c) A dark, dark rain cloud
d) A plague of locusts

Q48

CIRCA 1000 BC AROUND THE COAST AND
SOUTHERN ISLANDS OF SCOTLAND, WHICH OF THESE
LUXURIOUS FOODS DID PEOPLE *NOT* EAT?

a) Venison
b) Dolphin
c) Oysters
d) Wild raspberries

Q49

WHICH OF THESE IS A TYPE OF SHELTER BUILT
AROUND 750 BC?

a) All of the below
b) Crannog
c) Dun
d) Broch

KINGS EAT MEAT — PEASANTS EAT PORRIDGE!

SCOTLAND'S FAVOURITE TRADITIONAL FOOD IS A SLOPPY, STICKY, GRITTY, GREYISH SLUDGE CALLED PORRIDGE. IT'S MADE BY SOAKING OATMEAL (GROUND OR CRUSHED OATS) IN WATER FOR HOURS, THEN BOILING THE MIXTURE, WHILE STIRRING IT ALL THE TIME. THE STIRRING SHOULD ALWAYS BE CLOCKWISE — IN THE SAME WAY THAT THE SUN SEEMS TO CICRLE THE EARTH. PORRIDGE EXPERTS DON'T SAY WHAT MIGHT HAPPEN IF YOU STIR IN THE OPPOSITE DIRECTION, BUT THE PORRIDGE WOULD PROBABLY GO LUMPY. THE WATER SHOULD COME FROM A PURE MOUNTAIN SPRING, BUT THAT IS NOT ALWAYS POSSIBLE. TRADITIONALLY, PORRIDGE IS SERVED HOT, EITHER ALL BY ITSELF OR WITH A SPRINKLING OF SALT. IT SHOULD BE THICK ENOUGH TO CLING TO 'THE INSIDE OF YOUR RIBS'.

49

Q50

DURING THE IRON AGE WHAT DID CELTIC FARMERS NAIL OVER THEIR DOORS TO BRING GOOD LUCK?

a) A dog's head
b) A cow's head
c) A horse's head
d) A dormouse

IN SCOTLAND THERE IS NO SUCH THING AS BAD WEATHER — ONLY THE WRONG CLOTHES.

BILLY CONNOLLY (BORN 1942)

IN MY HEART

IN MY HEART, I SEE THE HIGH MOUNTAINS
I SEE, I SEE, THE TALL MOUNTAINS
I SEE, I SEE, THE STEEP VALLEYS
I SEE THE MISTY MOUNTAIN PEAKS.

I SEE, ONCE AGAIN, THE PLACE I WAS BORN
THEY WILL WELCOME ME THERE,
IN MY OWN MOTHER TONGUE
THERE I WILL FIND LOVE AND KINDNESS
PRICELESS TREASURES.

IN MY HEART, I SEE THE HIGH MOUNTAINS
I SEE, I SEE, THE TALL MOUNTAINS
I SEE, I SEE, THE STEEP VALLEYS
I SEE THE MISTY MOUNTAIN PEAKS.

TRANSLATED FROM THE ORIGINAL GAELIC WORDS COMPOSED
IN 1865 BY JOHN CAMERON OF BALLACHULISH

Q51

WHICH ANIMAL'S FACE AND FUR ARE TRADITIONALLY USED TO TRIM A SPORRAN?

a) Fox
b) Pheasant
c) Squirrel
d) Badger

Q52

WHICH OF THE FOLLOWING FOUR FESTIVALS CELEBRATED WARMTH, LIGHT AND LIFE?

a) Beltane
b) Lughnasad
c) Samhain
d) Imbolc

Q53

WHAT IS THE GRIMLY HUMOROUS ROMAN NAME FOR DEFENSIVE PITS FILLED WITH DEADLY, SHARPENED WOODEN STAKES HIDDEN UNDER BRACKEN AND HEATHER?

a) Snake pits
b) Lilia (lilies)
c) Vernonia (daisies)
d) Erica (heather)

SCIENCE AND TECHNOLOGY

SCOTS INVENTED LOGARITHMS, EXPLAINED ELECTROMAGNETISM, DISCOVERED THERMODYNAMICS AND CREATED MODERN CHEMISTRY. THEY ALSO GAVE US MEDICAL BREAKTHROUGHS FROM ANAESTHETICS AND ANTISEPTICS TO KIDNEY DIALYSIS AND ULTRASOUND.

Q54

WHAT TYPE OF DRINK IS MEAD?

a) Beer
b) Whisky
c) Cider
d) Honey wine

BRONZE AGE RECIPE

JELLY

1 FIND A PIECE OF HORN FROM A YOUNG DEER.*
2 BOIL IT IN WATER FOR SEVERAL HOURS.
3 REMOVE THE HORN AND LEAVE THE WATER TO
  COOL. IT WILL SET, LIKE A JELLY.

* Don't try this at home: animal horns can carry
  dangerous diseases – and you would be breaking
  the law.

Q55

WHAT IS WATTLE-AND-DAUB?

a) Woven twigs covered with mud or clay and animal hair
b) A breed of cattle
c) Strips of wood nailed horizontally across wall studs with plaster applied in between
d) A building technique using unfired mud bricks

Q56

THE CELTS DREAMED OF VISITING TIR NAN OG BENEATH THE WAVES, BUT WHAT DID IT MEAN?

a) The Land of the Lucky
b) The Land of Monsters
c) The Land of the Young
d) The Land of Magic

Q57

WHAT IS THE NAME OF THE WHITE, X-SHAPED CROSS ON A DEEP BLUE BACKGROUND, WHICH BECAME THE NATIONAL FLAG OF SCOTLAND?

a) The Saltire
b) The Christian Cross
c) The Crossbuck
d) The White 'X'

Q58

IN 1539, HOW MANY BOTTLES OF CLARET (RED WINE) DID SCOTS CARDINAL BEATON PURCHASE FOR HIS HOUSEHOLD?

a) 5,000
b) 22,000
c) 87,000
d) 165,000

Q59

WHICH OF THE FOLLOWING WAS A GENUINE VIKING FIGHTING TRICK?

a) Catching enemy spears in flight and hurling them back
b) Swinging a mighty two-handed battle-axe in a deadly surprise attack
c) Going berserk – stamping, shouting, wearing magic bearskins, eating poisonous funghi (which made them wild and fearless), chewing their shields in a rage, then stampeding wildly towards enemies
d) All of the above

PUZZLING LITTLE PIECES OF HOLLOWED-OUT PIGS' BONES WERE DROPPED AT MANY BRONZE AGE SITES. THEY TURNED OUT TO BE CHILDREN'S TOYS! WHEN TIED TO A PIECE OF STRING AND WHIRLED ROUND THE HEAD QUICKLY, THEY MAKE A LOUD ROARING AND BUZZING NOISE, GIVING THEM THE NAME 'BUZZ-BONES'.

Q60

WHAT IS DESCRIBED AS 'YELLOW, WITH A REARING LION IN RED, WITH BLUE CLAWS AND TONGUE, WITHIN A RED DOUBLE BORDER WITH FLEURS-DE-LYS FACING IN OPPOSITE DIRECTIONS'?

a) The Royal Standard of Scotland
b) The Scottish flag
c) The pattern on Magnus Bareleg's kilt
d) An emblem on the front of the first Scottish coins

 MUCH MAY BE MADE OF A SCOTCHMAN – IF HE BE CAUGHT YOUNG.

DR SAMUEL JOHNSON
(ENGLISH, 1709–1784)

THE WORLD COMES TO SCOTLAND!

ROMAN SCOTLAND WAS A MULTICULTURAL PLACE:

LOLLIUS URBICUS, THE ROMAN GOVERNOR IN CHARGE OF BUILDING THE ANTONINE WALL, WAS FROM ALGERIA. HIS WORKMEN INCLUDED SOLDIERS FROM THE BALKANS AND THE NORTH OF ITALY. SCOUTS SENT AHEAD OF ROMAN TROOPS TO SPY OUT THE LAND CAME FROM SPAIN.

THOUSANDS MORE ROMAN SOLDIERS LIVED IN FORTS ALONG HADRIAN'S WALL. THEY HAD BEEN RECRUITED FROM MANY DIFFERENT PARTS OF THE ROMAN EMPIRE: GERMANY, THE NETHERLANDS, FRANCE, BULGARIA, HUNGARY, SYRIA AND NORTH AFRICA.

TRADERS FROM ROMAN LANDS ALSO VISITED AND SETTLED SOUTH OF THE WALL.

BY LAW, ROMAN SOLDIERS WERE FORBIDDEN TO MARRY WHILE ON ACTIVE SERVICE. BUT MANY FELL IN LOVE WITH WOMEN FROM SOUTH-SCOTTISH TRIBES, AND HAD HALF-SCOTTISH CHILDREN.

Q61

WHAT IS INTERESTING ABOUT THE VILLAGE OF
SKARA BRAE, ON THE ISLAND OF ORKNEY?

a) It is the oldest village in Britain.
b) Only five people live there.
c) It has the largest island cathedral in Britain.
d) No animals are allowed there.

Q62

IN 1824, EDINBURGH BECAME THE FIRST CITY TO
HAVE WHAT?

a) Its own police force
b) Its own ambulance service
c) Its own fire brigade
d) Its own bowling alley

Q63

WHEN IT WHEN FIRST MENTIONED IN LITERATURE IN 1457, WHAT WAS THE SPORT OF GOLF CALLED?

a) goef
b) pinners
c) ball-hole
d) gowf

Q64

WHICH OF THESE FAMOUS AMERICANS HAS SCOTTISH ANCESTRY?

a) Ben Affleck
b) Matt Damon
c) Angelina Jolie
d) Brad Pitt

Q65

WHICH OF THESE IS NOT A CURRENT SCOTTISH LANGUAGE?

a) Scots
b) Scottish Gaelic
c) English
d) Norn

Q66

THE KAGYU SAMYE LING MONASTERY NEAR LANGHOLM, DUMFRIES AND GALLOWAY IS WHAT?

a) The largest Buddhist temple in Western Europe
b) The smallest Buddhist temple in Western Europe
c) The oldest Buddhist temple in Western Europe
d) The newest Buddhist temple in Western Europe

Q67

HOW MANY OF SCOTLAND'S 790 ISLANDS ARE UNINHABITED?

a) 30
b) 130
c) 230
d) 330

Q68

SCOTLAND HAS ABOUT THE SAME LAND AREA AS THE CZECH REPUBLIC, THE UNITED ARAB EMIRATES, PANAMA, THE US STATE OF MAINE AND THE JAPANESE ISLAND OF HOKKAIDO, BUT WHICH OF THESE HAS THE MOST COMPARABLE CLIMATE AND POPULATION DENSITY?

a) United Arab Emirates
b) Maine
c) Hokkaido
d) Panama

Q69

WANLOCKHEAD MINES, IN DUMFRIES AND GALLOWAY, POSSESS ONE OF THE GREATEST VARIETIES OF MINERALS IN EUROPE, BUT WHAT WOULD YOU FIND THERE?

a) Gold, copper, bronze, aluminium and lead
b) Lead, bronze, zirconium, sliver and gold
c) Bronze, magnesium, silver, gold and copper
d) Lead, zinc, copper, silver and gold

Q70

EDINBURGH IS EUROPE'S FIFTH-LARGEST WHAT?

a) Exporter of shortbread
b) Employer of women
c) Financial centre
d) Importer of chocolate

Q71

RUBISLAW QUARRY IS BRITAIN'S DEEPEST QUARRY, BUT JUST HOW DEEP IS IT?

a) 122 metres
b) 142 metres
c) 162 metres
d) 182 metres

Q72

GLASGOW TOWER IS THE TALLEST TOWER IN THE WORLD IN WHICH THE WHOLE STRUCTURE IS CAPABLE OF ROTATING 360 DEGREES, BUT JUST HOW TALL IS IT?

a) 107 metres
b) 127 metres
c) 147 metres
d) 167 metres

ANSWERS

PUTTING SCOTLAND ON THE MAP

Q1: D. 2,000

Scotland also has 790 islands, countless legendary monsters and a few real prehistoric fish – powan in Loch Lomond.

Q2: D. ISLE OF RUM

Here you can still see the tips of the very tallest mountain peaks that were completely buried under the ice around 18,000 BC!

Q3: B. 50

It was built from wood in around 3800 BC and measures 26 metres long and 13 metres wide.

Q4: A. CAIRNS

Barrows are actually huge heaps of earth.

Q5: D. 60 TALL STONES IN A CIRCLE

A project this big must have taken about 80,000 man hours to complete!

Q6: C. DAMNONII

At this time, the Celtic tribes were fiercely independent and there was no united Scottish nation. Each tribe has a different version of Celtic culture and they even spoke different – but related – languages.

Q7: A. 117 KM

When completed, the wall was painted white and marked with vertical red lines to give the impression of neatly trimmed blocks of stone.

Q8: A. ROB OF RISINGHAM

Today, historians actually think that 'Rob' was a woman – the Roman goddess Diana!

Q9: D. THE PICTS, SCOTS, BRITONS AND ANGLES

There was still no fixed border between Scotland and England, as those two nations did not yet exist.

Q10: B. THE FOOTPRINT STONE

In a grand gesture, the king would fit his foot into the hole at the top of the fort of Dunadd as a sign that he was master of the kingdom.

Q11: C. THE PICTS

The Picts also had a navy, which attacked Orkney in AD 681.

Q12: C. A 195-FOOT WOMAN

She was reported to have a body 'as white as a swan' and her hair was 18 feet (5.5 metres) long!

Q13: D. AD 565

Is she a snake? Is she a whale? Is she a dinosaur, surviving from 60 million years ago? Or is she just a pattern of waves, raised by wild winds blowing across the water? Today, she is one of Scotland's top tourist attractions – whether she exists or not!

Q14: A. LONGHOUSES

These were also known as 'black houses.' Houses of the same type built in north and west Scotland until around 1900, and many are still standing today.

Q15: B. VOE

Dale means 'valley', *Ness* means 'island' and *Wick* means 'bay'.

Q16: B. 16,000

For 500 years and more, English and Scottish armies fought over the border territory – the lands between the River Tyne and the River Forth. Soldiers from both sides advanced, attacked and retreated, as neither side could win a lasting victory.

Q17: A. MINUS 17°C

The very first Highland Games may have been held while Malcom's army was waiting to fight Macbeth. According to legend, Malcom organised races and other competitions to test the strength and fitness of his soldiers.

Q18: D. THE ABERDEEN HARBOUR BOARD

Around this time, the first towns were built in Scotland. King David was keen to encourage trade. Scots merchants sold fish, hides, wool – and coal, from Scotland's first mines. Most of their customers were from the Netherlands.

Q19: A. ST ANDREWS

Scotland's friends, the French, have a grim name for this sort of prison – *oubliette*. It means 'a place to be forgotten in'.

Q20: C. 10 MONTHS

She sent her men to drop huge rocks to crush English siege engines – and her maids to sweep the castle battlements, as if the war were nothing but a dusty nuisance.

O WAD SOME POW'R THE GIFTIE GIE US
TO SEE OURSELS AS OTHERS SEE US.

ROBERT BURNS (1759–1796)

THE LOCALS

Q21: A. MICKEY MOUSE

The population of Scotland is between 5 and 6 million; but around 13 million people of Scottish origin live in the USA and Canada, with millions more in Europe, Australia, New Zealand and many other parts of the world.

Q22: B. RED HAIR

Scotland still has the largest proportion of redheads in the world.

Q23: C. EMPEROR SEPTIMIUS SEVERUS

At first they appeared to be succeeding, but in 211 the emperor died and, without a leader, they retreated again.

Q24: A. Q-CELTIC

This is a similar language to modern Scottish and Irish Gaelic.

Q25: A. THE ANGLES

The Angles also built grand royal halls, made of wood, for their kings.

Q26: B. 3 AND 7

They also believed it was lucky to kill wrens, and the rowan tree was lucky because it kept witches away!

Q27: A. SELKIES

Kelpies are fierce, flesh-eating water horses, Banshees are wailing spirit-women and Glastaigs are kindly green women (sometimes half-woman, half-goat) who watch over children and farm animals.

Q28: C. ST ORAN

St Kentigern was also called St Mungo (Dear One) and founded a church at Glasgow. Today, Glasgow Cathedral stands on the site.

Q29: B. 300

Books were written on vellum – cleaned, smoothed calfskin. The minerals used to make the monks' paints included lead (for red) and arsenic (for yellow). Both are poisonous, and could make their users very ill, ulcerating their skin and rotting their bones.

Q30: A. AMERICA

They were slaves of Viking-ruled Scotland, and part of an expedition led by Icelander Thorfinn Karlsefni. He was hoping to find new places for Vikings to live, in Vinland (the Viking name for Newfoundland, Canada), but was driven away by bad weather, fights with Native Americans and quarrels among the settlers.

Q31: C. KING OF THE PICTS

After five years of fighting the Picts, he invited the last surviving Pictish prince to peace talks – and killed him!

Q32: D. MACBETH HAD A WICKED WIFE

Macbeth also did NOT murder King Duncan in his bed, go half-mad with guilt or see moving forests and ghostly daggers.

Q33: D. SHE DID ALL OF THE ABOVE

She is also reported to have spent hours in a damp, dark cave praying, and also paid for a ferry to help pilgrims reach St Andrew's tomb.

Q34: C. SHE DIED OF A BROKEN HEART

As her coffin was carried past Malcom's tomb, it mysteriously became too heavy to move – and so they were buried side by side.

Q35: A. MAGNUS BARELEGS

Magnus Barelegs was a Viking earl who wanted more land. Edgar the Peacable told Magnus he could have all the land he could sail around. Magnus sailed round all the Hebrides islands, then got his men to carry his boat across a narrow strip of land in the far south-west – and won the Mull of Kintyre.

Q36: B. SEVERE SEASICKNESS

She had a plate of royal sweeties to comfort her on the crossing from Norway to Scotland, but the ship hit a storm. The winds and waves were treacherous and terrifying and poor little Margaret died as her ship reached Orkney.

Q37: C. RED JOHN COMYN

Bruce lost his next battle against the English – some said this was God's punishment for murder. He fled to a cave to hide.

Q38: B. OF LEPROSY

The name 'leprosy' covered a range of skin diseases in Bruce's time, some mild and some very serious. Traditional treatments included medicines made from plants, gold or spiders, and water from holy – or magic – wells.

Q39: D. SHE WORE IT LIKE A JEWEL

She also founded Sweetheart Abbey near Dumfries, as a place where the heart, and she, could be buried.

Q40: C. ONE THIRD

Scotland's cold climate meant that the fiercest, most contagious 'pneumonic' form of the disease developed. It was passed on by coughs and sneezes, and victims were reported to 'swell up and die' within two days.

SCOTS, WHA HAE WI' WALLACE
   BLED,
SCOTS, WHAM BRUCE HAS AFTEN
   LED,
WELCOME TO YOUR GORY BED
OR TO VICTORIE...

ROBERT BURNS (1759–1796)

WORK
AND PLAY

Q41: C. *ENCYCLOPAEDIA BRITANNICA*

'A dictionary of arts and sciences, compiled upon a new plan.'

Q42: A. SCOTCH EGG

The Scotch egg is said to have been invented by London department store Fortnum and Mason. The bicycle was invented by blacksmith Kirkpatrick MacMillan, the waterproof coat or 'mac' was named after its inventor Charles Mackintosh and Sherlock Holmes was created by Scotttish doctor Sir Arthur Conan Doyle.

Q43: C. A TYPE OF ROCK

This can be found on the Isle of Lewis.

Q44: B. A BAGPIPE

The bagpipes are the only national instrument to have been legally recognised as a weapon of war.

Q45: C. SEAWEED

Do not try this – some stones explode when heated.

Q46: D. COPPER AND TIN

It could be melted and poured into moulds to make beautiful jewellery, sharp weapons: axes, knives and Scotland's very first swords.

Q47: A. ASH AND GAS FROM HEKLA VOLCANO

The sound of the eruption could even be heard in Scotland!

Q48: B. DOLPHIN

Rare coprolites (fossilised human poo!) found in Shetland show that Scotland's farmers had a healthy diet: whole grains, fish, wild berries and lamb.

Q49: A. ALL OF THE BELOW

Crannogs are round wooden houses on artificial islands in the middle of lakes or bogs; brochs are tall round stone towers without any windows; and duns are walled or fenced enclosures in places that are naturally well defended, such as clifftops.

Q50: C. A HORSE'S HEAD

The Celts were head-hunters and believed that each creature's spirit lives in its skull – sometimes they would even nail an enemy's head over their door!

Q51: D. BADGER

A sporran is a traditional part of male Scottish Highland dress; it is a pouch that performs the same function as pockets on the pocketless Scottish kilt.

Q52: A. BELTANE

Celtic farmers marked the four seasons of the farming year with four festivals. Some are still celebrated today – especially Samhain (All Saints' Day) – although their original meaning has been forgotten.

Q53: B. LILIA

This defensive measure protected the Antonine Wall, which is made from slabs of turf piled on a rock foundation; it stretches for 60 km and is 2.75 metres high.

Q54: D. HONEY WINE

Kings gave lavish feasts, with mead, meat, music and storytelling. In return for this royal generosity, warriors were expected to fight and die for their king.

Q55: A. WOVEN TWIGS COVERED WITH MUD

A change in climate brought colder, wetter weather and houses made of wood and turf were hard to keep weatherproof.

Q56: C. THE LAND OF THE YOUNG

For the Celts, Scotland was an enchanted land, full of ghosts and spirits. They thought they saw floating islands, and hollow hills where the *sidhe* (pronounced 'shee'), or fairies, lived.

Q57: A. THE SALTIRE

In AD 735, just two years after St Andrew's bones had reached Scotland, Pictish soldiers fighting against the Angles saw a huge white cross against the bright blue sky. It looked just like the cross on which St Andrew had been crucified. The Picts believed the saint was fighting on their side, and won the battle!

Q58: D. 165,000

Colonies of Scots also moved to live in wine-growing regions of south-west France (there is a whole Scottish suburb of Bordeaux), buying vineyards, making wine, speaking French and paying French taxes.

Q59: D. ALL OF THE ABOVE

They also fought like wild boar. Warriors charged in a boar-snout (V-shaped) formation called *svinfylking*, with shields overlapping and spears bristling.

Q60: A. THE ROYAL STANDARD OF SCOTLAND

In the language of heraldry this is described as 'Or, a lion rampant Gules armed and langued Azure within a double tressure flory counter flory Gules.'

Q61: A. OLDEST VILLAGE IN BRITAIN

The stone houses of Skara Brae have built-in dressers where farmers kept precious possessions such as pottery bowls.

Q62: B. AMBULANCE SERVICE

Princes Street Gardens, situated in the city centre, boasts the world's oldest floral clock and the Royal Botanic Garden Edinburgh contains Britain's tallest Palm House in The Glasshouse Experience.

Q63: D. GOWF

No-one knows where it originated, or when it was first played in Scotland. But by around 1600, the Scots themselves called it their own 'peculiar diversion' (special sport).

Q64: A. BEN AFFLECK

Affleck is a Scottish surname: it derives from Auchinleck and represents one of the pronunciations of that name. It may be pronounced with the stress on either syllable.

Q65: D. NORN

Norn is a Germanic language once spoken in Scotland. Scottish English occasionally borrows words from Scots or Scottish Gaelic.

Q66: A. LARGEST BUDDHIST TEMPLE

It was founded in 1967 and was the first Tibetan Buddhist centre to have been established in the West.

Q67: B. 130

Scotland has over 790 offshore islands, most of which are to be found in four main groups: Shetland, Orkney, and the Hebrides, subdivided into the Inner and Outer Hebrides.

Q68: C. HOKKAIDO

Hokkaido, formerly known as Ezo, Yezo, Yeso, or Yesso, is Japan's second-largest island; it is also the largest and northernmost of Japan's 47 prefectural-level subdivisions.

Q69: D. LEAD, ZINC, COPPER, SILVER AND GOLD

Until 1799, some workers, such as coal miners, could be bought and sold by factory owners, like slaves or domestic animals.

Q70: C. FINANCIAL CENTRE

In 1947, Edinburgh hosted a month-long party. Held every year since, the Edinburgh Festival is now the world's greatest arts celebration.

Q71: B. 142 METRES

Rubislaw Quarry was opened in 1740 and is located at the Hill of Rubislaw in the west end of the Scottish city of Aberdeen.

Q72: D. 127 METRES

It holds a world record for being the tallest tower in the world in which the whole structure can rotate a full 360 degrees.

A VERY PECULIAR HISTORY
QUIZ BOOKS

OTHER TITLES IN THIS SERIES:

EGYPTIAN MUMMIES
LONDON
BRIGHTON
CHRISTMAS
KINGS AND QUEENS

A VERY PECULIAR HISTORY

TITLES IN THIS SERIES:

WILLIAM SHAKESPEARE	TITANIC
SCOTTISH CLANS	THE TUDORS
SCOTTISH WORDS	SCOTLAND VOLUME I
SCOTTISH TARTAN	SCOTLAND VOLUME 2
ROBERT BURNS	LONDON
CHARLES DICKENS	CASTLES
THE 60S	IRELAND
FISHING	BRIGHTON
CRICKET	CHRISTMAS
GOLF	VAMPIRES
WHISKY	ANCIENT EGYPT
THE OLYMPICS	WALES
WORLD WAR ONE	GLOBAL WARMING
WORLD WAR TWO	RATIONS
QUEEN ELIZABETH II	THE BLITZ
VICTORIAN SERVANTS	KINGS AND QUEENS
YORKSHIRE	GREAT BRITONS

www.salariya.com
where books come to life!

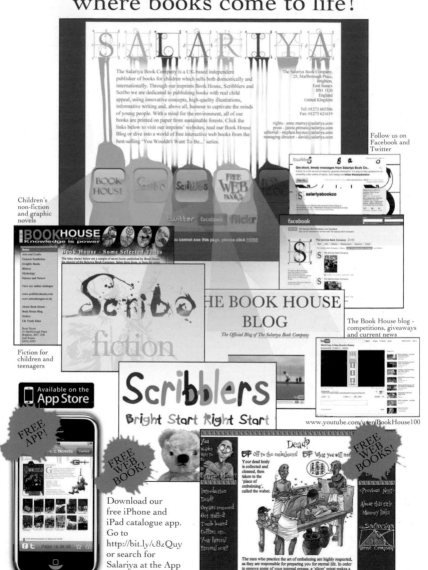

The Salariya Book Company is a UK-based independent publisher of books for children which sells both domestically and internationally. Through our imprints Book House, Scribblers and Scribo we are dedicated to publishing books with real child appeal, using innovative concepts, high-quality illustrations, informative writing and, above all, humour to captivate the minds of young people. With a mind for the environment, all of our books are printed on paper from sustainable forests. Click the links below to visit our imprints' websites, read our Book House Blog or dive into a world of free interactive web books from the best-selling 'You Wouldn't Want To Be...' series.

The Salariya Book Company,
25, Marlborough Place,
Brighton,
East Sussex
BN1 1UB
England
United Kingdom

Tel: 01273 603306
Fax: 01273 621619

rights - anne.murray@salariya.com
press - jamie.pitman@salariya.com
editorial - stephen.haynes@salariya.com
managing director - david@salariya.com

Follow us on Facebook and Twitter

Children's non-fiction and graphic novels

Fiction for children and teenagers

THE BOOK HOUSE BLOG
The Official Blog of The Salariya Book Company

The Book House blog - competitions, giveaways and current news

Scribblers
Bright Start Right Start

www.youtube.com/user/BookHouse100

Available on the App Store

FREE APP!

FREE WEB BOOK!

FREE WEB BOOKS!

Download our free iPhone and iPad catalogue app. Go to http://bit.ly/c8zQuy or search for Salariya at the App Store

Four free web books